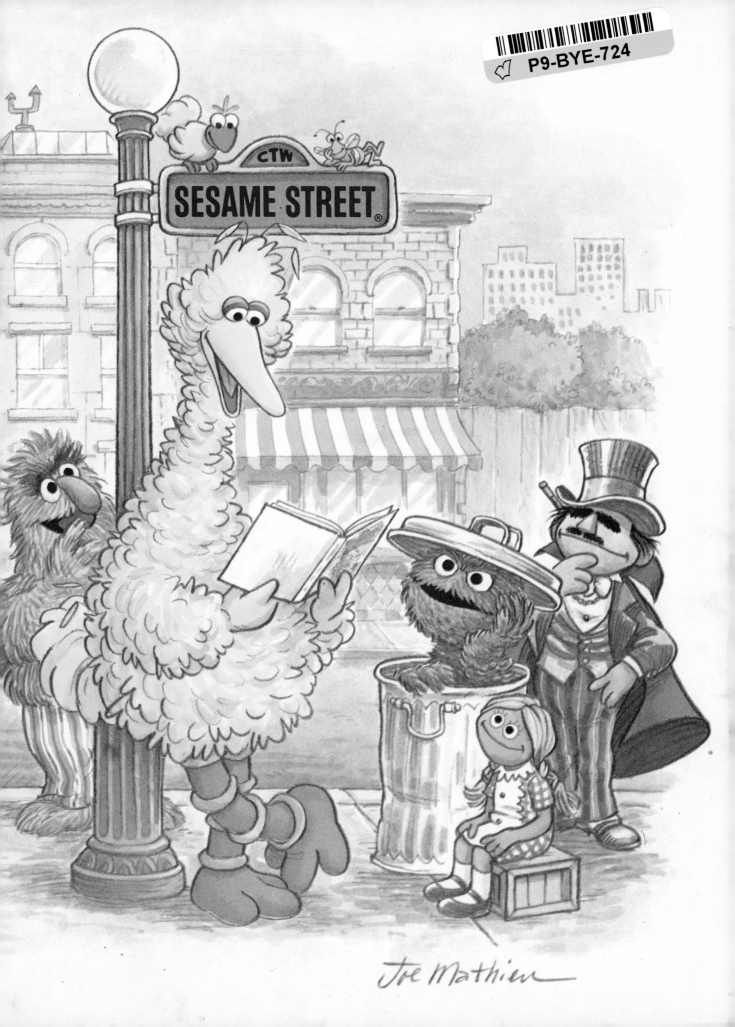

Joe Mathieu

THE SESAME STREET® LIBRARY

With Jim Henson's Muppets

VOLUME 4

FEATURING
THE LETTERS
G, H AND I
AND THE NUMBER
4

Children's Television Workshop/Funk & Wagnalls, Inc.

WRITTEN BY:

Michael Frith
Emily Perl Kingsley
David Korr
Sharon Lerner
Nina B. Link
Jeffrey Moss
Norman Stiles
Daniel Wilcox

ILLUSTRATED BY:

Mel Crawford
A. Delaney
Michael Frith
David Gantz
Joseph Mathieu
Jon McIntosh
Harry McNaught
Marc Nadel
Michael J. Smollin

PHOTOGRAPHS BY:

Charles P. Rowan

Happily, a Young-Hero-Cowboy lassoed Penelope with his trusty rope...

Unhappily for Penelope, she slipped, and rolled down a hill, wrapping the rope around and around her.

Luckily, Penelope came to a stop just before she rolled into the ocean.

As luck would have it, Penelope was now
lying across a railroad track…
…and a train was coming.
The train was getting close.

Ernie! How do I
get out of this?

The train rumbled closer. If only a Kindly-Old-Hero-Switch-Operator would throw the switch and send the train careening off on another track.

The Great Sesame Street Alphabet Show

ABCD...
First—the Incredible
Alphabet Acrobats!

EFGH...
Next—the Great Bert
and his sensational flying PIGEONS!

IJKLM...
Here is the fantastic
Balancing Bird—oops!

NOPQ...
And now—The Amazing Mumford's
Magic Letters—
A la peanut butter sandwiches!

RSTUV...
Presenting Oscar and his Wonder-worms,
starring SLIMEY as the letter S!

WXYZ...
And last of all... The Mighty Monsters!
What a show!

Cookie Monster's Alphabet Cookies

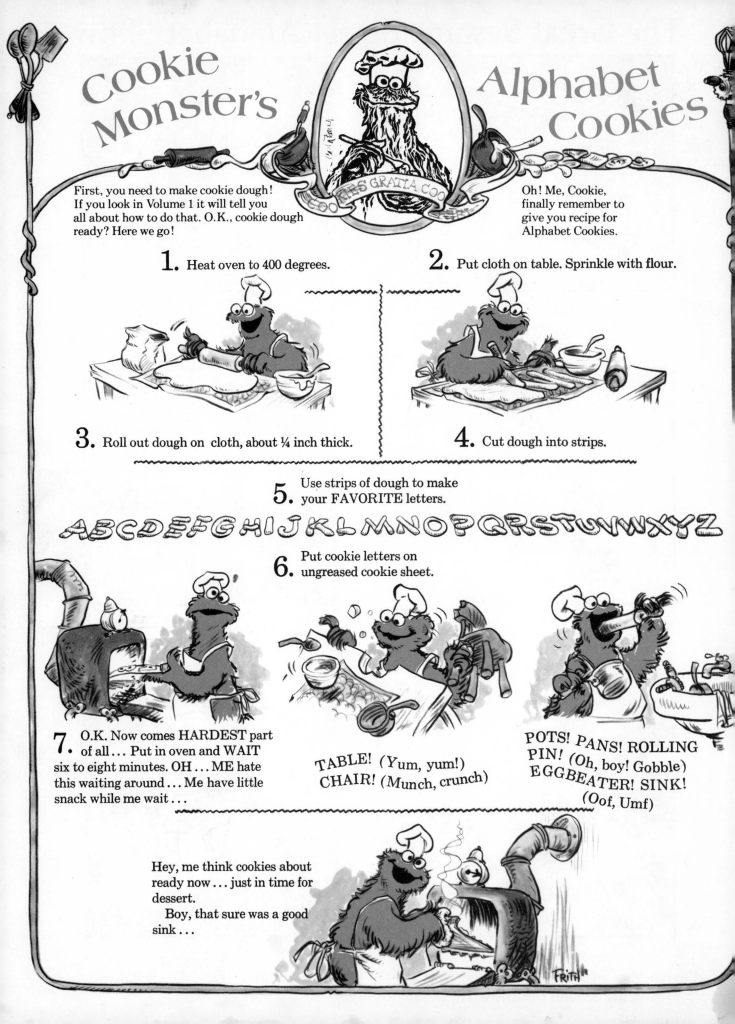

First, you need to make cookie dough! If you look in Volume 1 it will tell you all about how to do that. O.K., cookie dough ready? Here we go!

Oh! Me, Cookie, finally remember to give you recipe for Alphabet Cookies.

1. Heat oven to 400 degrees.

2. Put cloth on table. Sprinkle with flour.

3. Roll out dough on cloth, about ¼ inch thick.

4. Cut dough into strips.

5. Use strips of dough to make your FAVORITE letters.

ABCDEFGHIJKLMNOPQRSTUVWXYZ

6. Put cookie letters on ungreased cookie sheet.

7. O.K. Now comes HARDEST part of all... Put in oven and WAIT six to eight minutes. OH... ME hate this waiting around... Me have little snack while me wait...

TABLE! (Yum, yum!)
CHAIR! (Munch, crunch)

POTS! PANS! ROLLING PIN! (Oh, boy! Gobble) EGGBEATER! SINK! (Oof, Umf)

Hey, me think cookies about ready now... just in time for dessert.

Boy, that sure was a good sink...

FRITH

Hi! I'm Roosevelt Franklin and I really know my shapes. Here's a groovy game about shapes. It's called

GUESS WHAT I FOUND

First, get some friends to play with you. Then look around the room and choose something square, like a box or that windowpane. Don't say the name of the thing, but shout out, "Hey, I looked around, and guess what I found. I found something . . . *square!*"

Your friends have to try to guess what it is. They say . . .

I looked around. Is this what you found . . . The table top?

The book?

The window-pane?

Right ON, Baby Breeze!

The first one who guesses what you found gets to choose a new shape and a new thing, like maybe a door that's a rectangle, or a clock that's a circle.

The great thing about this game is that you can play it anywhere.

MCINTOSH

Prairie Dawn, Bus Driver

Jack and the Beanstalk

Jack's poor mother sent Jack to market to sell a cow for money. He sold the cow for beans instead, which made his mother so angry she tossed the beans out the window.

The next day a huge beanstalk had grown up. It seemed to touch the sky. Jack climbed the stalk and at the top he found a large castle. He had just enough time to hide before an enormous giant came in.

"Fee-fi-fo-fum! I smell the blood of an Englishman!" roared the giant. He looked and looked, but he couldn't find Jack. So he ate a large meal instead. Then he took a small goose from the closet and told her to lay some golden eggs for him.

As soon as the giant fell asleep, Jack grabbed the goose and the eggs and slid down the beanstalk.

"Good boy, Jack," said his mother when she saw the golden eggs. "Those beans were useful after all."

The next day Jack went up the beanstalk again. This time he wasn't so lucky. He tried to steal the giant's golden harp. But the harp cried out, "Master!" and the giant woke up.

Jack ran for his life. The giant ran after him. But Jack slid down the beanstalk and chopped it down with an ax.

The giant tumbled to the ground and that was the end of him. As for Jack and his mother, they had so much gold they never had to worry again.

Oscar and the Number Four

My name is Oscar the Grouch and my favorite number is the number 4. Let me tell you 4 reasons why.

First of all, I like the number 4 because there are 4 wheels on a garbage truck. Count them. And I love garbage trucks because of all the wonderful yucchy trash inside!

I also like the number **4** because a skunk has **4** legs.
Count them. A skunk makes a terrible smell that makes
everybody run away. Heh-heh.

A table has **4** legs, too. And a
table is a perfect thing to sit at
when I eat my strawberry ice
cream sundae with pickles
and sardines on top!

And last of all, I like the number **4** because the page of a book has **4** corners. Count them. And after you count the corners, turn that page and then I won't have to look at you any more!! *Good-by!*

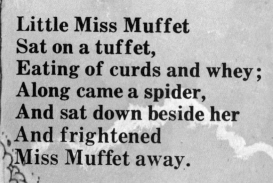

Little Miss Muffet
Sat on a tuffet,
Eating of curds and whey;
Along came a spider,
And sat down beside her
And frightened
Miss Muffet away.

FIRE! FIRE!

There's a fire in the hot dog cart.
Help Fireman Ernie get to the fire
so he can put it out.

 Egad! I see through my magnifying glass that these People in my Neighborhood are each missing something. They need a good detective.

What's Missing?

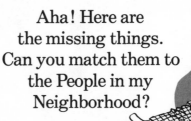

ICE CREAM

US MAIL

Aha! Here are the missing things. Can you match them to the People in my Neighborhood?

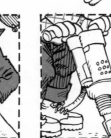

The Count Inks an I

Greetings!

I am the Count. I am here in this book to show you the letter **I**. I will make the letter **I** with this ink. **Ink** begins with the letter **I**. But I'll bet you knew that already.

There! This is the letter **I**. One poor lonely letter **I**. I will make another.

There! Two letter **I**'s. Ha. Ha. Ha. Now, let me see…

Four thousand, two hundred
and twenty-one
letter **I**'s…

Four thousand, two
hundred and twenty-two
letter **I**'s…

Oh, it's WONDERFUL!

Ha, ha, ha.

Four thousand, two hundred
and twenty-three…

That Alphabet Cookie recipe looks great. It was worth waiting for.
Ernie

It sure was. I hope every-body tries it before they get too busy reading Volume 5.
Bert